More Scripture Memory Songs
Learning God's Word Through Music

Teaches The Names Of Jesus' Twelve Apostles!

Table of Contents

S0-AQK-398

Credits:

Written By: Kim Thompson, Karen Hilderbrand, Hal Wright
Arranged By: Hal Wright
Engraving By: Practical Music Services
Cover Photography By: Virginia Dixon

Companion Products:

TWIN 138CD   More Scripture Memory Songs CD   ISBN# 1-57583-279-8
              (Split Track)
TWIN 138   More Scripture Memory Songs Cassette   ISBN# 1-57583-280-1
              (Side 1–Stereo, Side 2–Split Track)

Twin Sisters Productions, Inc. • 2680 W. Market Street • Akron, OH 44333 • 1-800-248-TWIN (8946)

I Can Do All Things

I can do all things through Him who gives me strength.
Philippians 4:13

Words and music by
Kim Thompson, Karen Hilderbrand and Hal Wright
Arranged by
Hal Wright

I can do all things through
Him who gives me strength! Philip - pi - ans four, thir - teen.

Romans 3:23

For all have sinned and fall short of the glory of God.
Romans 3:23

Words and Music by
Kim Thompson, Karen Hilderbrand and Hal Wright
Arranged by
Hal Wright

For all have sinned— and fall short— of the glo-ry of God,— Ro-mans three, twen-ty three.—

For all have sinned— and fall short— of the glo-ry of God,— Ro-mans three, twen-ty three.— But

Call On The Name Of The Lord

Everyone who calls on the name of the Lord will be saved.
Romans 10:13

Words and Music by
Kim Thompson, Karen Hilderbrand and Hal Wright
Arranged by
Hal Wright

Call on His name._____ Call on His name._____
Lift up His name._____ Lift up His name._____

_____ Ev - 'ry - one who calls on the name_____ of the Lord_____
_____ Ev - 'ry - one who lifts up the name_____ of the Lord_____

So we call on His name,—— we will shout and pro-claim—— that Je-sus is Lord.—— Je-sus is Lord!—— Call on His name.——

1x lighter, 2x fuller

Call on His name.

Ev - 'ry - one who calls on the name of the Lord will be saved,

will be saved.

I Will Trust In You

When I am afraid, I will trust in You. In God,
whose word I praise, in God I trust; I will not be afraid.
Psalm 56:3-4

Words and Music by
Kim Thompson, Karen Hilderbrand and Hal Wright
Arranged by
Hal Wright

No Other Name But Jesus

Salvation is found in no one else, for there is no other name, under heaven given to men
by which we must be saved.
Acts 4:12

Words and Music by
Kim Thompson, Karen Hilderbrand and Hal Wright
Arranged
Hal Wright

Sal - va - tion is found____ in no____ one else,____ for

for God pro - vid - ed a way.___ No oth - er name,___

He sent His Son___ to pay___ the price,___

for there is no oth - er name___ but

23

I Will Praise You

I will praise You, O Lord, with all my heart; I will tell of all Your wonders.
I will be glad and rejoice in You; I will sing praise to Your name, O Most High!
Psalm 9:1-2

Words and Music by
Kim Thompson, Karen Hilderbrand and Hal Wright
Arranged by
Hal Wright

praise You,___ O Lord,___ with___ all my___ heart;___ I will

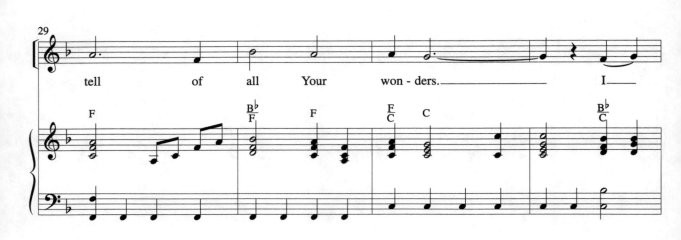

tell of all Your won - ders._____ I___

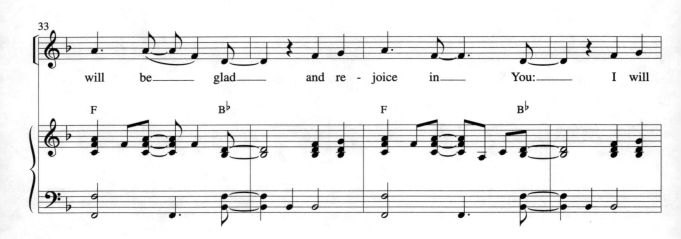

will be___ glad___ and re - joice in___ You:___ I will

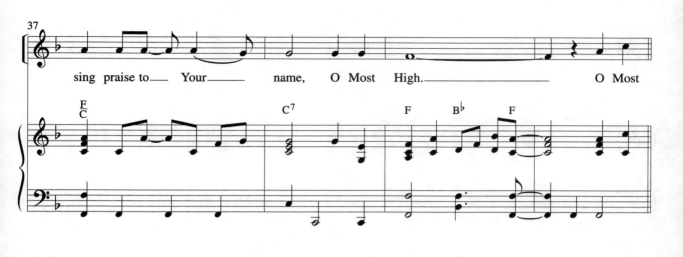

Love Is Patient And Kind

Love is patient, love is kind.
I Corinthians 13:4

Words and Music by
Kim Thompson, Karen Hilderbrand and Hal Wright
Arranged by
Hal Wright

I Am The Light Of The World

I am the light of the world. Whoever follows me will never walk in
darkness, but will have the light of life.
John 8:12

Words and Music by
Kim Thompson, Karen Hilderbrand and Hal Wright
Arranged by
Hal Wright

__ shine, I'm gon-na let my light___ shine,_

_I'm gon-na let my light___ shine for Je - sus,_

gon - na let it shine!

The Lord Is My Rock

The Lord is my rock, my fortress and my deliverer; my God is my rock,
in whom I take refuge, my shield and the horn of my salvation.
He is my stronghold, my refuge and my Savior.
II Samuel 22:2-3

Words and Music by
Kim Thompson, Karen Hilderbrand and Hal Wright
Arranged by
Hal Wright

The Twelve Apostles

These are the names of the twelve apostles: first Simon (who is called Peter) and his
brother Andrew; James son of Zebedee, and his brother John; Philip and Bartholomew;
Thomas and Matthew the tax collector; James son of Alphaeus, and Thaddaeus, Simon
the Zealot and Judas Iscariot, who betrayed Him.
Matthew 10:2-4

Words and Music by
Kim Thompson, Karen Hilderbrand and Hal Wright
Arranged by
Hal Wright

for I want the world to see, that the king - dom of God is near! Re -

pent— and be - lieve. Now— go and preach the Word. Share what you've learned from me."

Twelve a-pos-tles came in all, quite dif-'rent all would seem, to share the mes-sage of the Lord, for

oth-ers still were fish-er-men. One was thought to doubt the Lord, they must have be-come friends.

Si - mon Pe - ter, and his bro - ther An - drew, James the son of Zeb - e - dee,

and his broth - er John, Phil - ip and Bar - thol - o - mew, then there's doubt - ing Thom - as,

Love One Another

Love one another. As I have loved you, so you must love one another.
John 13:34

Words and Music by
Kim Thompson, Karen Hilderbrand and Hal Wright
Arranged by
Hal Wright

four.

Clap Your Hands

Clap your hands, all you nations; shout to God with cries of joy!
How awesome is the Lord, Most High,
the Great King over all the earth!
Psalm 47:1-2

Words and Music by
Kim Thompson, Karen Hilderbrand and Hal Wright
Arranged by
Hal Wright

High, the great King o - ver all the earth. How

awe - some is the Lord Most High, the great

King o - ver all the earth. Clap your

God with cries of joy!___ Clap your hands, all you na - tions; Shout to

God with cries of joy!___ Clap your hands, all you na - tions; Shout to

God with cries of joy!___ Clap your hands, all you na - tions; Shout to God with cries of joy!___

Notes

Notes

Notes

Notes

Notes